BETHLEHEM'S
G·I·F·T

LEONARD H. BUDD

FAIRWAY PRESS
628 S. Main St. • Lima, Ohio 45804

BETHLEHEM'S GIFT

FIRST EDITION
Copyright © 1989 by
Leonard Budd

7694 / ISBN 1-55673-176-0   PRINTED IN U.S.A.

But you, O Bethlehem Ephrathah,
  who are little to be among the clans
  of Judah,
from you shall come forth for me one
  who is to be ruler in Israel,
whose origin is from of old,
  from ancient days.

                              Micah 5:2

Foreword

Found in a Williamsburg, Virginia shop, rooted in the early years of this nation, is a little card with this Christmas greeting:

Chriftmas is more than a day at the end of the year
More than a day of joy and good cheer
Chriftmas is really God's pattern for living
To be followed each day by unfelfifh giving
Then Peace on Earth will come to ftay
When we live Chriftmas every day.

That perspective wraps every day of the year in the red and green of the Christmas season, and has us recalling God's gift at Bethlehem as an endless outpouring of divine love. Every year, as the brightness of the Christmas season is defused with the return of old routines, we say, "I wish the spirit of Christmas would stay all year long!" That, too, is the message of this little book of Christmas stories. They can be entertainment and teaching all at once. They certainly may be read on Christmas Eve, but any time can value the remembrances of Christmas. They are different ways of looking at God's special gift of the Christ child. Four of the stories are make-believe. One is a true life adventure.

The Church of the Saviour Foundation has made possible the publication in this book, and the Church Growth Work Area of this Cleveland congregation has aided in its preparation. Particularly, Dr. Daniel Schubert, Dr. Earl Anderson, Dr. and Mrs. Ralph Dessem have guided this project to completion. Mrs. John Twist, Executive Secretary at the church, shared in the final reading. The cover photograph is the center piece of The Nativity Window in Myers Chapel of Church of the Saviour, placed there in memory of John M. Morgan and Elizabeth Lee Morgan. The illustrations at the beginning of each chapter are adaptations of portions of The Nativity Window. The illustrations are by Daniel Jankowski.

The stories are dedicated to two daughters whose own experiences with Christmas have been great times of happiness and sharing, and whose own futures will be brightened with God's Gift begun at Bethlehem. May Christmas Day be every day for Julie and Ellen, pictured with their mother, Karen, in the photograph at the beginning of chapter five.

Leonard H. Budd

It will be said on that day, "Lo, this is our God; we have waited for him, that he might save us. This is the LORD; we have waited for him; let us be glad and rejoice in his salvation!"
Isaiah 25:9

The Hope Held

The sun was just setting toward the Western Sea as Rabbi Joab settled down by the side of his home to begin the evening prayers. His prayer shawl, with white tassels on each corner, was pulled closer around his neck. The night had begun moving the winds from the desert into the village. Bethlehem was set on a ridge that pulled the winds from the Dead Sea depths, bringing them up and over the ridge height every evening as the sun disappeared into the Great Sea.

The day was finished, except for the prayers, and Joab began the chants he knew so well, chants that marked his leadership of the little village. He had been taught in Jerusalem, in the Holy City, at the Great Temple. Bethlehem was proud of its rabbi.

The night was quiet. Birds had now settled down from their farewell songs to the sun. Distant flocks of sheep were bleeting more quietly as sleep settled into their companies, aided by the songs of shepherd boys.

Bethlehem was surrounded by great grazing lands. The rabbi put his head back against the wall and looked out over those pastoral fields. "How beautiful," he thought. "How beautiful is that land given by God. Surely this is the promised land. How great a God to give so wondrous a gift as this land, and to give it to his special people—his chosen."

On the road to Jerusalem, just at the point where it begins its descent over the hill, a fire flashed to light. Its sudden brilliance meant that the soldiers had thrown a cup of oil into the kindling. Although it was too far away to see, the rabbi knew that the soldiers of Rome would be standing around the flames. The fire would warm their hands and armor as a new company began its watch of the road.

9

Joab took a deep breath, a sigh that was shared by Jews through that region. God gave them the Promised Land, but God did not give them Rome. Within the beauty of the land, amid the valleys and flocks and beautiful sunsets over the Great Sea, was the hard, foreign-voiced presence of Rome. The Romans did not belong here. Their taxes, their slavery, their foreign ways were anathema to the Jews. Not only did they flaunt their graven images upon themselves and every building and road sign, but they worshipped a Roman god and defiled the places of God's chosen people.

As thoughts came more quickly to the rabbi, he shook his head, as if to escape the rising hatreds that came with the thoughts. "Why has God done this? When will we be free? When will God's promises come true?"

A sound of sandaled footsteps within the house broke the bleak brooding of the rabbi. His wife, a good woman who had been born in the village, came to the doorway. "Rabbi," she said, using the title in respect for his evening prayer time. "Rabbi, do not let the night air give you the sickness. Come into the house and speak your prayers."

"Soon, woman." Joab's words were warmed by his respect and admiration for Naomi. She had been named for a famous woman of Bethlehem. It was Naomi of old who had gone to Moab with her husband and son, Boaz. When the famine had passed and when the menfolk of the family had died, Naomi returned to Bethlehem with her daughter-in-law, Ruth. The rabbi's wife shared the name of Naomi, and the hometown.

The rabbi continued his prayers, speaking the singsong phrases in a voice that caressed each word. There was comfort in these words, and in the saying of the words — the repetition of rituals. The prayers continued until the darkness was complete and the birds and sheep were deep in their own rest for the night. All was well. The night would bring refreshment.

As the rabbi rose to follow the advice of his Naomi, the sound of soldiers broke the quietude. Soldiers were making

10

an unexpected inspection. "Awake," they cried as they banged the doors of the village houses. "Awake to be counted!"

Sleepy villagers arose, bundling themselves in cloaks, and made their way outside their houses, to stand in huddled groups for the count. The tall soldiers of Rome would make their notation and move to the next house.

In such a manner they came to the rabbi's house to count the bearded leader and his Naomi. It might have been courage brought by the prayers, or the anger of having the pastoral scene shattered by the unnecessary counting, or perhaps it was a call for action initiated by God. Whatever, the rabbi stood straight and said, "Do not bother us. Go away!"

Men had been killed by Rome for saying less. The soldier stopped, unsure of what he had heard in the Hebrew tongue, but certain that the words were not meant kindly. His sword was drawn, and with a swift motion he brought the handle down upon the rabbi's shoulder. Joab fell to the ground. With no further word, the soldier moved on to the next family census.

Naomi helped the rabbi back into the house, gently guiding him to lie upon the mat that had been laid out for the night's rest. It was painful for him. Perhaps a bone was broken. He could not move his arm more than a handspan. As was his custom from rabbinic training, he began speaking words of scripture. The phrases called upon God to be a strength to him against all enemies — the soldier, of course, but also the pain that lodged in his shoulder.

With the soldiers now gone from the village, the people hurried to the door of the rabbi's house. Word had spread with the winds from the desert that he had received the soldier's blow and had been helped into the house by Naomi. They whispered words of concern for Joab and muttered words of hate against the tall, armor-coated occupants of their land.

The rabbi's quotation of scripture soon turned to a time of teaching. That was his training, of course. He lay upon the mat and began telling of the long history of his people. It was a story that any one of the villagers could have told, for it was not only their history, it was their hope as well.

The story recounted the trek of Abraham from a distant land into the Promised Land, the digression to Egypt, the miraculous escape led by Moses, the covenant of Law that was given by God. The story told of kings and prophets who ruled the people, of Saul and David, of Jeremiah and Isaiah. The story turned into a mournful chant as foreign nation after foreign nation became the oppressor of his people — Assyria, Babylon, Egypt, Rome. Words spit out loathsome curses.

The story then mellowed into pleading words: "When, O God, will the deliverer come? O God of Abraham, Jacob and Isaac, when will you release us from the bondage of oppression?" Tears came to those who stood in the doorway, and tears worked their way down the cheeks and beard of the rabbi as he spoke.

It was a youth by the door who broke the sad litany of words. "But rabbi, when will God act?" It was a well-meaning question, but young boys just did not interrupt the rabbi when he was in the full bloom of his teaching. "When, rabbi?"

The rabbi reached for his aching shoulder, as if to plead a reason for giving no answer. Yet he did answer. "The scriptures do not tell us. We must wait — and wait patiently. The Messiah will come. He will drive out the Romans. He will restore the Kingdom of David. And we shall be free once more. You will see. The Messiah will come. It is promised, and God never breaks a promise."

There was silence in the house. "Go now, all of you, and pray in your homes that Messiah will come soon. Pray to God that deliverance will be seen with the light of tomorrow. Pray hard. The Messiah, our Saviour, will come!"

They left the house, returning to their own homes with such petitions to God close upon their minds. Naomi bent to rub the rabbi's shoulder and to ease a cushion behind his head. Soon there was silence in the village. Each person was engrossed in thoughts that shaped his destiny. When will God's Messiah come? Will Messiah lead an army to drive the Romans into the Great Sea? Will God's messenger carry a double-edged sword and hurl a spear farther than anyone else? Will the Savior of God's people kill to save? Will he move into the Roman palaces at Jerusalem? Will he govern as Rome and place guards on the roadways? Will he come to the doorways of village houses and strike at the heads of old men? What is Messiah to do? How does a Savior save? What is redeemed by a Redeemer?

The little town of Bethlehem slept restlessly that night. The stars moved overhead on their appointed paths. The flocks in the fields rested under the careful watch of the shepherds. But the people of Bethlehem were busy meditating upon God's ways, and the advent of those ways in the lives of God's people. Does God force his will? Will the Savior's strength be rough or gentle? Will Messiah lead with a sword or with a word?

Little Bethlehem slept in the quiet night. Yet of all the thoughts dreamed in those hours, of all the hopes prayed, none dared envision the place of little Bethlehem in God's scheme of things. The Messiah would come with the gentleness of a baby born in Bethlehem. God's messenger would meet those same Roman soldiers. But the Messiah would conquer, and in the conquering he would reveal the Word above the sword. The shalom of God has the power of great armies. Rabbi Joab was right. God keeps his promises!

Again Jesus spoke to them, saying, "I am the Light of the world; he who follows me will not walk in darkness, but will have the light of life." The Pharisees then said to him, "You are bearing witness to yourself; your testimony is not true." Jesus answered, "Even if I do bear witness to myself, my testimony is true, for I know whence I have come and whither I am going, but you do not know whence I come or whither I am going. You judge according to the flesh, I judge no one. Yet even if I do judge, my judgment is true, for it is not I alone that judge, but I and the Father who sent me. In your law it is written that the testimony of two men is true; I bear witness to myself, and the Father who sent me bears witness to me." They said to him therefore, "Where is your Father?" Jesus answered, "You know neither me nor my Father, if you knew me, you would know my Father also."

John 8:12-19

Sharing The Birth

I am elderly now, gray haired and bent over. But I remember times of my youth when I raced over the Bethlehem hillsides. My playmates could not catch me. I was that fast. It was my job in those days to gather firewood, collecting it from the hillsides near the town. I gathered the branches that the winds broke from the trees, and the twigs and blowing thatch that caught in the little gullies of the land. I would bring that rough collection to the Inn and place it by the large oven. It was often hard work for there was little wood on those hillsides of Judea. Most had already been cut away, or eaten away by the herds of sheep and goats. Yet, day after day, I would run over the hillsides hunting out the firewood in so short supply.

As I sit in my shop now I can still remember the cold evening, with the Inn filled, when the two of them arrived. There was no room for ones who came so late. Even then the evening sun was below the horizon. In that day the decree had brought so many people to Bethlehem. Even money could not buy space. There was no room. Yet, seeing her condition, the Innkeeper just could not shut the door. So he offered what he had — the stable! It was a cave behind the Inn, deep enough to provide shelter from the wind. The animals within provided warmth. It certainly allowed for resting. It was protection from the chill that moved across the grazing lands — a chill that brought shivers to the younger shepherds out under the stars.

It was in that stable that the baby was born. Only the father and mother were present — and the animals. And me, a small boy on an errand for more firewood. I watched in wonder as a human child entered life. Little wonder that I remember the moment and its sheltered site within the cave. But there was more that I remember. I recall the tenderness of the father. My mind holds his image even today — even when the other parts of the event are remembered only as distant, shadow images. I hold the image of that father in my mind even now!

17

I can picture his touch of gentleness as he held his wife and that tiny infant. I can hear his cries of support, his words of concern. Fathers, we are told, are suppose to be harsh and distant and commanding. But this father was not. He was strong, to be sure, but his strength was in his compassion and tenderness and caring. Throughout the long night he held his young wife and the child, holding them within the coarse-woven cloak that was his only coat.

After the baby was born I helped light a small fire by the cave's entrance, using the twigs and sticks from my gatherings. I stayed with them as the flames warmed the night air and held it captive within the cave. The urgency of my own tasks did not seem so important that night.

There were other strange things about the event. I saw shepherds from the western fields come into that place and stand as if in the presence of a great personage. Later the town was to talk of foreign royalty that made a caravan to the cave and did homage to the little newborn life. The royal three soon departed from Bethlehem. So did the peasant three, leaving in a great hurry. They did not return northward, but quickly, before the warmth of the sun was felt, headed toward the land of pyramids. The father led the animal with its precious cargo. Again, he showed his concern for his wife and the care of the child. As I have said, the father of that family was a special remembrance to me. I have held it all my days. It is as if some message is waiting in that remembrance.

And here I am now. I reside in Jerusalem. I am not collecting firewood, but selling oil for lamps. My shop is near Damascus Gate, away from the pillars of the Temple, just where the noon sun casts a hard shadow from the Gate's stone arch. I sell the oil that lights the homes of Jerusalem and gives them warmth. But I do not have an easy time. My oil is good. My prices are fair. The weights are true. Yet, I have barely enough business to live. Why? Because I am shunned! My Jewishness is only a heritage, not a practice. I believe another way now.

Yet, I do not complain for I have other treasures, treasures more important than business and sales. These greater treasures are a knowledge of God and a fellowship with Christ Jesus. I am a Christian. It is a new fellowship in this old city. We believe — no, we know — that Jesus of Nazareth is the Son of God. He is the Messiah we have long sought. He is "God with us," our Emmanuel, our salvation. In Christ, resurrected from earth's death, we see God! In fact, whereas the pagans only fear God, and our Jewish brothers only ritualize God, we know God as our Heavenly Father! When Jesus was living on earth and when he began his teaching at the Sea, he taught us to pray, "Our Father in heaven . . ." He said, "How much more your Heavenly Father cares for you . . ." that knowledge of God is all that matters to me now, far more than the sale of oil.

It was new, this freshness of Jesus to speak of God as Father. He taught us that Father God was our creator and protector, concerned for us, loving us, guiding us. What a change from the carefully constructed phrases of the leaders in their endless debates: "No more than two hundred paces, Caleb! Remember, it is sabbath!" Bah. Jesus said that, too. "Bah. The sabbath is made for man, not man for the sabbath." Jesus taught other things in the great creation of our Heavenly Father. He taught with stories and deeds. Where I once was indifferent about everything, now I believe in something. Where I once worried about everything, now I trust. It is called, within our Christian family here, "the peace that passes all understanding." I used to emphasize the dark and dismal. Now I see light where I never saw it before. That, too, was Jesus' teaching. He once spoke of himself as the "light of the world." He meant that his Heavenly Father was seen through him. But then, quickly, he turned around, pointing a finger away from himself. "You," he said, "are the light of the world." I remember he pointed at me! I try to be just that, because I want to be known as a Christian. I want to show that God is a Heavenly Father to me.

19

As I sit by the door of my shop, remembering the early years of youth, I try to talk with those who will slow their pace. I say, "You can be a Christian, too. Not like the Pharisees who would have you be a proper Jew, with regulations for every second. No. You can be a Christian if you understand what Jesus meant when he taught 'I and the Father are one.'" I say to those who will listen, Jesus said, 'Let your light shine before men and women and children in such a way that your good works will be appreciated and praise will be given to your Father in heaven.'" It seems these days that my words about Jesus are as much my work as the selling of oil.

But sometimes I wonder why my mind recalls that father in the Bethlehem stable whenever I talk of Jesus' words of Father God. Why does my mind drift back to that long ago time even when I seek my Heavenly Father in prayer? Why is it that when the crisp night air settles up against the walls of Jerusalem, like tonight, that I find my mind moving back to that nameless child and mother, and that very special father? Is there some connection that I do not understand? It was just a baby. Even with the awed shepherds and the pageant of wisemen, it was just a baby. And it was a tired and very young mother. And it was just a father, a father who stooped to touch the woman's shoulders, and to hold the so-small child, and to care. Somehow I think there is a tie — and a message for nights like this. Perhaps that night heralded more than the birth of the baby. I wonder on nights like this as I sit by the door of my shop, as I try to talk with those about me, and as I look upon the dark sky alive with the lights of heaven. In my wondering I give praise to my Heavenly Father for all his gifts, for Jesus his Son, for life and life evermore!

*In the beginning was the Word, and the Word was with
God, and the Word was God. He was in the beginning with
God; all things were made through him, and without him was
not anything made that was made. In him was life, and the
life was the light of men. The light shines in the darkness, and
the darkness has not overcome it.*

*The true light that enlightens every man was coming into
the world. He was in the world, and the world was made
through him, yet the world knew him not. He came to his own
home, and his own people received him not. But to all who
received him, who believed in his name, he gave power to be-
come children of God; who were born, not of blood nor of
the will of the flesh nor of the will of man, but of God.*

John 1:1-5, 9-13

The Light

The cold comes quickly across the Judean hillside. Once the sun is rimmed against the western mountain range it quickly disappears and the cold comes to fill every space of that stony landscape. The cold enters the sleeves of the travelers, and up underneath the long cloaks, and in around the neck. It is a biting cold, pushed along by a wind intent on reaching the distant heights in record time. With that cold comes the darkness.

Bethlehem was no different that night from any other night. The sun settled out of sight. The cold moved through the village streets. And with the cold there was the darkness. Doors were fastened shut with leather straps. Windows of wood or animal skin were sealed tight. The fire in the center of the common room of the Inn was stirred to make more heat. The little son of the Innkeeper carried in arms-full of thatch and carefully herded logs to build the fire higher. It was a crowded Inn in Bethlehem. Roman law had mandated a registration. It was ordered that every man go to his home town to record his name. Those with money stayed in the warmth of the Inn. Those without money stayed where they could, as best they could.

It does not take much imagination to see Joseph and Mary approaching Bethlehem as the sun settled to the mountain top and as the darkness enveloped the land. It was the last of a troublesome trek from Nazareth. They pushed the donkey and themselves those last miles, determined not to sleep again upon the cold ground under the meager protection of an olive tree. "Just over the hill, Mary. Just over the hill and we will find the Inn." Joseph spoke to his young wife. In that expectation they went those last miles — encouraged by the dream of a warm fire and the faithfulness of the little donkey that Mary rode.

23

But, as we now know, there was no room. The words of denial were shouted through a cracked door even as the darkness of the night filled the street. "No room here," said a busy Innkeeper. "All filled. Go somewhere else. Be gone." The expectation of warm lodging was not to be fulfilled that night. But another expectation would be, Mary had sensed in those last miles that this would be the time. Her first child would be born in the hours ahead. It would not matter whether the room was warm or not, nor if there was a room or not!

Joseph knew it, too. Again he knocked on the door, asking now for only his wife. "She is to give birth this night. Do you not have a place for her?" This time there was a hesitation in reply. The pause came as if a battle between compassion and self-centeredness was being fought within that tired Innkeeper. His voice now was softer. "To the back then. To the stable."

The little donkey moved with care those last steps around the squat building of clay and stone, back beyond the lean-to shed that held the Inn's stores, back away from the Inn toward the rocky hillside, back deeper into the darkness of that cold night. The stable was not seen. It was smelled and heard. The stars did not shine into that cave where the animals were herded and tied. With difficulty Joseph felt along the stone wall with his hands and along the dirty and wet floor with his feet. He sought a space upon which Mary might rest. Deeper and deeper he went into the cave, kicking aside the beasts he found. But he could find no space for Mary. He returned to say that once more the field would be their bed and the tree branches their roof.

As he returned he saw a tiny flame come from the back of the Inn. Illuminated by the flame was the face of a child. The flame moved up and down as the child moved toward the stable. Up. Down. Up. Down. As the child drew near Joseph could see the little lamp held carefully in two small, pudgy hands. "My Master sent this light, sir. He said to return it in the morning. My Master said there is water at the far end of the stable — water for the animals that you may use. My

Master said, Peace to you." The little child's speech was welcomed, as was the light. With the passage of the lamp from the child's little hand to the carpenter's large and rough hand, the child ran back through the darkness to the Inn.

With the flame burning brightly, Joseph was able to find a place for Mary and to keep the animals away. The light was both comfort and protection. It was an instrument of salvation — that tiny, single flame.

In the morning hours Mary delivered her first-born child, a boy, and wrapped him in the tight swaddling clothes that were understood to protect him even as had the womb. Joseph had cleared a little place down near the water and had found in the stone a little identation that he filled with new straw. There Mary and the little baby lay. Joseph had also found a way to fasten the lamp up on the stone wall so that its light shown down upon Mary and the so-tiny baby. It was that light, that little flame, that the baby first saw. His first view of earth was of the little flame that burned from the wick soaked in the oil. The flame danced as the winds moved into the deep parts of the stable. At times it almost went out. But it never did. It always remained that flame. And while newborn babies eyes do not see in great detail, there was for that baby's eyes the little light from the little lamp in that little stable behind the Inn of Bethlehem.

Later, when the baby was grown to manhood and the mantle of Messiahship was upon his shoulders, his words would sometimes use the images of fire, of flame, of lamps set upon stands that all in the house might have light. God intended, he taught, for humanity to live by the light. Can it be that there is a tie? Jesus spoke then, and to us, about light that moves into our lives so that all darkness is pushed aside. The darkness of discouragement, the darkness of despair and loneliness, the darkness of fear are overcome by the light of God's love. And that love of God is shared. "Let your light shine, that others will praise God because of the light in your life." (Matthew 5:16)

In his preaching ministry, set in the grandeur of the Jerusalem Temple, Jesus looked upon the crowds and said, "I am the light of the world, (those) who follow me will not walk in darkness, but will have the light of life." (John 8:12) Some who heard him argued and set about plans for his crucifixion. But others who heard his words understood that in his compassion, and in his trust of God, light for the living of life was to be found! And his light did illumine their daily living.

Indeed, when John set about writing his Gospel he did not tell about shepherds in the fields, nor of wisemen who trekked the sands of the east. John told of the birth story in terms of light.

> *All that came to be was alive with his life, and that life was the light of (humankind). The light shines in the dark, and the darkness has never mastered it!*

> *(John 1:4-5)*

That is the Christmas story! Where there was darkness there now is light. Where there once was aimlessness and selfishness and loneliness there now is purpose and charity and love shared. Where there once was no eternal hope, there now is a gift of salvation to eternal life. It comes to us with the birth of Jesus. The little flame, carried into the stable to light a birth was moved out of the stable to light the world!

Herod summoned the wise men secretly and ascertained from them what time the star appeared; and he sent them to Bethlehem, saying, "Go and search diligently for the child, and when you have found him bring me word, that I too may come and worship him." When they had heard the king they went their way; and lo, the star which they had seen in the east went before them, till it came to rest over the place where the child was. When they saw the star, they rejoiced exceedingly with great joy; and going into the house they saw the child with Mary his mother, and they fell down and worshiped him. Then, opening their treasures, they offered him gifts, gold and frankincense and myrrh. And being warned in a dream not to return to Herod, they departed to their own country by another way.

Matthew 2:7-12

The Day After

Just before dawn there is a very quiet time. It is a silence over the landscape, as if nature is holding its breath in anticipation of a new day. The birds have not yet awakened. The sun is still traveling below the horizon line. The winds are still, not yet moving through the tree tops. In that moment before the start of a new day, when all is silent and quiet and poised for another beginning, little Joshua was getting up. His night's sleep had been interrupted in such a strange and dreamy way that he had hardly rested at all. Now, as the sun was about to rise, he stirred, rubbed the hot redness from his eyes, and began the walk to the other side of town.

Bethlehem was a beautiful place, crested upon the hill that was surrounded by shallow valleys. The valleys were filled with the vineyards, the olive orchards, and the grazing lands. Each night, with the flocks protected and the work of the fields completed, little fires could be seen by the houses of Bethlehem — fires that dotted the hillsides just as the stars dotted the heavens above.

In the springtime the scent from the olive trees would be blown across the fields and up to the houses of Bethlehem. Only the smell from the baking ovens would be more welcomed than the fresh, clean, perfumed smells that came across the fields and up to the doorways of Bethlehem.

Joshua was ten years old. He had been born to a poor woman, living in the great city of Jerusalem. When he was seven his mother had arranged for him to be cared for by a family in Bethlehem. Although it was only six miles away, he had seen his mother just three times. Once she had visited him in his new home, and twice he had been able to travel with a caravan to the Holy City, seeing her there and then returning next day to his work in Bethlehem.

The reason he stirred so early, with such great attention to the sun's rising, was that he worked for Bethlehem's innkeeper. It was his job to see that all the animals in the stable were fed, watered and cleaned — and to see that the work was done before the first guest left the Inn. Because some of the guests left with the first light of day Joshua worked by the very faintest of the sun's rays shining through the stable doorway.

On this particular morning, because of his restless night, he was late. He ran all the way, passing the breadmaker (by whose profession all of Bethlehem was named), passing the town center where the two roads crossed. The Inn was on the other side of town, half attached to the houses that lined the single roadway and half rooted in the great fields that stretched down the hillside and out over the valley toward the Holy City. Joshua reached the Inn just as the first edge of the sun popped over the eastern hill. He raced around the corner of the Inn, bare feet spring-like, and ran breathless through the stable entry.

Each day Joshua could guess how many donkeys were in the stable simply by the smell. Sometimes a horse was there, too, tethered to an iron peg that had been driven into the wall by a Roman soldier. Occasionally, sheep were quartered in the stable, although it was too small for a whole flock. This day Joshua discovered that he was not the first person there! And he soon learned that had he arrived on time, at his usual time before the sunrise, he still would not have been the first there.

Joshua did not know what to do. No one had told him about a stable that housed human beings. He had listened carefully to all the Innkeeper said, but nothing had ever been said as to what he, Joshua, was to do if he found a man and a woman asleep with the donkeys — and especially if he were to find a little baby asleep in the very straw that he must use for his cleaning!

But that is what he found. Within the shelter of the stable there was a man, a young woman, and a very tiny baby. All were asleep until the moment that his bare feet landed upon the dirt floor of the stable and caused everything within to awaken: a horse pegged to the wall, two donkeys at the far end of the shelter, and the four sheep that were nestled together at the other end of the stable. The man was instantly on his feet, uncertain of the commotion, but certain of his role as protector. The woman stirred, reaching a hand toward the little baby nestling close. Joshua stood still. He tried to think of what he, stable boy to the Inn, must do.

"It is just a child, Joseph," said the woman. "He will bring no harm." The man relaxed, yet looked beyond the boy to see if more would follow his bounding footsteps. "We were allowed here," continued the young woman, speaking now to Joshua. "The Innkeeper gave the right." Joshua nodded his understanding. Cautiously he walked to the little nest of straw that held the baby. "Is this your baby? Was the birth here?" he asked. With sounds so near, the baby opened dark eyes and moved a little hand in the quick, rushing motion of the newborn. Joshua had never seen a baby so small, so beautiful, so perfect. He had never been that close to an infant of humanity. His babies were of donkey and sheep, of the goats that were everywhere. As he looked down upon the little child, his mind recalled words from his restless night's sleep, words that had come to him as if overheard or half-heard. "For to you is born this day, in the city of David, a Savior which is Christ the Lord." It was remembered as a song, a wonderful song with melody that echoed across the sky.

Joshua spent all day in the stable. Usually he was through with his work by mid-morning. By the time the sun was high he was on his way home, running from shadow to shadow to capture the cool shade. But this day Joshua stayed at the stable. He puttered around with the animals, watching them leave one by one. He carried in new straw, and brought water from the single well that served all of Bethlehem. But mainly, he watched the baby — that tiny, beautiful baby.

Somehow news of the baby's birth spread through the village. "Born in the stable, he was," was the common exclamation. "Born so poor. His parents not even of Bethlehem."

It was on this day after the birthnight that two visitors arrived. Both were known to Joshua for they were all the same age — born under the same moon was the report. The first was Sari, the little daughter of the Innkeeper of Bethlehem. Sari kept the three rooms of the Inn in good order, for the work of the woman must rest with the daughter when the mother is dead. Sari's mother died two years before, died of the swelling. Sari could close her eyes and still see the pale and anguished face of her mother on the day she died. Sari did not like to think of it, but could not help herself. Every time she straightened that room of the Inn — as her mother had — the image would be before her. She did her work quickly, in that room. Too quickly, her father said.

The word of the baby's birth must have early been shared by those within the Inn, for Sari came to the stable as the first of the guests left that morning. She sat with Joshua and watched for a long time as the baby slept. She saw the mother gently hold the infant, feed him, and wrap him in the bits of cloth that were his first clothing. All at once Sari was on her feet and bounding out the doorway. She raced back to the Inn. Later she told how troubled she had been that the family was so poor, and the baby so lovely. Her child-spirit said she must do something to help.

Her plan, carried out with great speed, was to bring one of the little lamps from the Inn and place it above the manger where the baby was sleeping. The lamp was partly for light, although the daylight gave enough light to the stable. What Sari was concerned with was the smell of the stable. Her little lamp soon had the fragrance of frankincense filling the shelter. It brought the aroma of some far-off place of beauty — and of reverence, for the smoky smell was part of the priestly act in the Great Temple of Jerusalem. The young mother, still lying in the bed of straw, breathed deeply at the sweet smell that filled the stable. The little baby followed the flickering flame, watching the light jump higher and higher as the wick turned. Sari joined Joshua in a corner of the stable, watching the Mother and Child. They both were learning about life's caring, life's love, life's responsibility for life.

About mid-day, as the young mother was busy with the feeding of her son, a second visitor came to the stable. Eli was the son of the baker in Bethlehem. He knew that someday he would be the baker himself — as were his father, his grandfather, and generations of the family before. Indeed, "Bethlehem" meant "house of bread." It was assumed, at least by Eli's family, that, therefore, they had started the town. They were careful not to make much mention of the claim, though, for Bethlehem was "David's City" — the home of King David, King of Israel and all Judah. No one dared claim an equal inheritance.

Eli sometimes watered the camels of the traders, and the horses of the soldiers, as they paused in their journey at the well of Bethlehem. It was an exciting job for a young boy, coming so close to the world travelers of that age, and to the armor-coated soldiers of Rome. Eli would brag often about the adventure, elaborating upon simple stories told by the travelers, and often finding that his imagination placed himself in the center of some intrigue.

Once, when a trading caravan from across the desert stopped in Bethlehem, the bearded and dirty camel driver shouted to Eli to water all the animals and win himself a coin. Sure enough, when the wheezing and dirty beasts of the sands had about emptied the Bethlehem water supply, Eli was given a coin. He did not know its value. It was worn, but still the image of a flower could be seen on one side and the image of a man on the other. Eli had kept the coin hidden away, but often he would uncover it just to look at it, and to polish it more.

Now, here was Eli, coming close to the mother and father of the little baby born so poorly, and handing his special coin to the father. "It is for the baby," he said. "It is for the baby at his birthing. Every baby is to have a gift." Joseph took the coin, recognizing the intensity of Eli's words. With the coin in his hand, Joseph said, "But this is a gold coin. Do you wish the baby to have so great a gift?" Eli had made up his mind, "Yes. Keep it for the baby so that you can say he was born rich — just like a king."

As the three children sat watching the new baby, Joshua became more and more uncomfortable. There was the lamp's flame, and the fragrance about the stable. There was the gold coin, even now in the hand of Joseph. What could he give? He had nothing. He was an orphan boy from Bethlehem — with only a stable skill to offer. To anyone watching him, it was very evident that Joshua was feeling a great sadness, an emptiness as the hours of the day wore on. The three children stayed in the stable, now talking freely with Joseph and his young wife, Mary. They each had held the baby so carefully. Each had sung a song to encourage the infant's sleep. Each had told a bit about themselves — including the mother and father with tales about their distant city of Nazareth, and the special hopes they had for their child now sleeping. And, of course, there had been the gifts given.

Finally, the shame of the reflecting was too much. Joshua ran from the stable. He raced away from the homes of Bethlehem and out into the grazing fields. They were familiar and comforting fields. All three children roamed the hills, knowing the terrain like the women knew the curves of their own water jugs. It was a knowledge so exact that three water jugs looking exactly alike could be lined up in a row on the well's edge, and each woman would pick her own jug without thought. Such was the knowledge of the hills about Bethlehem to little Joshua.

In the sweep of the fields, Joshua came upon a lovely looking shrub. It was a scrubby brush of a bush, with whitish flowers and little green sprouts that formed a frame for each flower. "That is it," he thought. "I can bring a flower." He grabbed great handfuls of the "roserock" that grew wildly. He raced back across the rough land to the entrance of the stable. "Here is my gift," he shouted — quickly hushing his voice as he saw the baby stir. "This is my gift to the little baby. Is this all right?" His question was understood by Mary who put her arms around Joshua, hugging him tightly. "Of course," she replied, "the myrrh is very pretty and my little Jesus will like it." It has its uses, too," she added, looking at Joseph. Joshua did not know it, but the oil from his little plant-gift was used in preparing bodies for burial. Joshua only saw the lovely flowers. It was a gift of beauty, not meant as a gift of foreboding. Mary knew that, as did Joseph.

Now each had given a gift to the baby Jesus. Gold. Frankincense. Myrrh. It is reported from other quarters that Kings came into the stable and presented such gifts to the Christchild. They were great wisemen from distant places who had traveled long days guided by the stars of heaven. And who is to say, for it is written thus!

But for this day after, in the poorness of a cattle stall, here were three gifts given by children. Perhaps there is a mingling of remembrances — for with that Christ-child's birth, the wisest can be very simple and childlike, and the kingly can be very common. There was new understanding perceived in the days following that ancient birth. It was a new message to the world, a new understanding of what was powerful and fully truthful, of what life was meant to be. That understanding would someday come to Joshua and Sari and Eli. But for now, on the day after, they were content with just being there, sharing the moment, and sharing the gifts.

And in that region there were shepherds out in the field, keeping watch over their flock by night. And an angel of the Lord appeared to them, and the glory of the Lord shown around them, and they were filled with fear. And the angel said to them, "Be not afraid; for behold, I bring you good news of a great joy, which will come to all the people; for to you is born this day in the city of David a Savior, who is Christ the Lord. And this will be a sign for you: you will find a babe wrapped in swaddling cloths and lying in a manger." And suddenly there was with the angel a multitude of the heavenly host praising God and saying,

    Glory to God in the highest, and on earth peace
    among men with whom he is pleased.

When the angels went away from them into heaven, the shepherds said to one another, "Let us go over to Bethlehem and see this thing that has happened, which the lord has made known to us." And they went with haste . . .

(Luke 2:8-16)

Twenty Centuries Later

It looks, to the Western eye, more like a field of rock than grazing land for the sheep and goats of Israel. It is covered with tawny grasses, squat shrubs and an occasional cluster of silver-green olive trees. It has remained unchanged through the two millennia since shepherds heard a wondrous message of a baby's birth. Today there are modern intrusions like barbed wire, and Coca Cola machines, and telephone poles that spike the air in orderly lines. But the earth is shallow and filled with the rocks of Creation that break through the sod in irregular patterns. It was in a cave formed by those intruding rocks that shepherds sought refuge from the wind and cold of night. Perhaps it was even such a cave that protected the birth of the baby Jesus.

The bus, another of those modern intrusions, carries us from the height of Jerusalem along a ridge road that once was boundary between Arab and Jew. Shell holes still mark the buildings, and at one point a small, worn plastic sign says, "Beware of mines." Along that road the bus moves with considerable speed and the signs of an ancient Palestine whiz by: a camel laden down with branches for home fires; a small boy, *keffiyen* wrapped around so that only his eyes are seen; square and squat houses built on top of and out from the rock of the land; road signs pointing to the Shore, the Negev, the Dead Sea. Our bus moves over roadways that once carried Crusader troops and Roman legions and Egyptian armies. Today more troops use it — but pilgrims, too, as of old. This road carried wisemen from the court of Herod in Jerusalem. Did they look at the same contour of hill? Did they stop to buy fruit from a wayside peddler? Did they watch the sun set toward the Mediterranean Sea just as did our bus load of modern tourists? It is an awesome road — this ridge road from Jerusalem to Bethlehem.

Traffic slows. Police have set their barricades halfway across the road. A checkpoint. In modern Israel your license plate tells a story. It tells by color whether you are Arab or Jew. It tells by letter your city. Depending on your license plate you are either waved on or stopped for checking. The plates of our bus, and its modern lines, tell another story. We are tourists this night, visitors from afar, following our own spiritual stars to Bethlehem.

These days Bethlehem is a Christian city, and Arab. It is part of the "occupied land," by Arab feelings, and is marked so on the maps given by the Israelies. Its center is Manger Square — a great court before the Church of the Nativity. High above the square, atop that bastion of a church, stands the tower with the bells. You have heard them through the miracle of radio as they sound each Christmas Eve. Below the bells, off the courtyard, is the low entrance to the Basilica. It is an Eastern Orthodox building tied to a Roman building and both involving priests of the Coptic, Syriac, Armenian, Greek and Roman traditions. Each sect goes about its own business in a careful ignoring of the others. Inside the church the rituals, incantations and fevered recitations of ageless prayers take place. Part of the Nave dates back to Constantine (a.d. 326), making it the oldest Christian Church in continuous use.

For many persons this Church of the Nativity is a place of ancient dreams. A visit culminates a pious life. Below the high altar, entering from the stone steps to the right, steep steps and low ceiling, we move down into the grotto. Tonight the walls are covered with gold cloth. Sharp light and acrid smoke from candles mingle in the small area. Here in this cave under the altar, the pious are told, Jesus was born. "You are now in the stable. Here, under this stone, is the manger where he lay after the ordeal of birthing. Here, touch the silver star that marks the spot. Light a candle. Say a prayer. Kneel." One with British accent, chooses to sing instead; "Joy to the world, the Lord has come!"

Perhaps the grotto underneath the high altar of that very ancient church is the place of Jesus' birth. Perhaps. But Mary

40

and Joseph would never recognize it. Yet, they too would have been hushed in some ageless awe to see the reverence and care given by bearded priests who move to straighten a sagging gold hanging, to trim a flickering lamp, to stoop and pick up a small, castoff box inscribed with the words, "Kodacolor 126."

From this small cavern, ten by thirty feet, the steps rise quickly to the chancel floor and then into a modern Roman Sanctuary where television lights shine down upon a rehearsal. Priests of that tradition walk through the solemn service that will be televised at midnight. Yet, even the practice brings silence to the flocking tourists. Hymns and carols of the season echo from the high valuts of the nave. The steps of the priests are metered. And one, caught yawning, brought to the scene a sense of routine. We walk out of the church, into the expanse of Manger Square, and back to our bus.

It moves us through the narrow streets of Bethlehem, then along a tiny uneven road to the herdsmen's village of Beit Sahur. This little town, attached to Bethlehem as a suburb, holds another ancient and pious site. Here is Shepherd's Field and a cave that might, perhaps, have also been the place of Jesus' birth. The land is rocky. The sheep crowd in. In the shelter of the rocks and near a manger of rock, the baby could have been born that long ago night. Mostly Protestants crowd this field tonight. They sing the carols in voices accented by Europe and America, by England and Asia, Africa, Arabia. Jesus is One Lord, One Savior. It is a Silent Night, a Holy Night.

Saint Nuit, Nuit Silencieuse
Noche de Paz, Noche de Amor
Stille Nacht, Heilege Nacht
Silent Night, Holy Night

The sun was going down upon this stretch of rocky field. Houses in distant villages begin to shine with electric light. To shepherds long ago those lights would have been as miraculous as an angelic chorus. There is no ritual here, as there had been in the buildings of Bethlehem's center. Instead there is the unity

41

of voices in familiar words of song and in familiar words of scripture:

> *And there were shepherds in the same*
> *country, abiding in the field,*
> *keeping watch by night over their*
> *flocks . . . And they came with haste,*
> *and found Mary, and Joseph, and the*
> *baby lying in the manger.* (Luke 2)

Students sat upon a northern wall, their backs to the darkening fields. They sang and listened. They wore that universal blue denim uniform, with hiking boots and fleece-lined jackets. A youthful United Nations honored the birth of Jesus. Some of them would sleep the night on this hillside. Others would crowd into Manger Square to hear the midnight bells that sound in Bethlehem and over the radio waves to the world.

A Dutch lady had walked from Jerusalem — a mere six miles — but she was in her 75th year. She had visited this Holy Land in her retirement, only to desert her tour and stay. That was ten years earlier. Now she lives the hard life on an Israeli *kibutz*. With knapsack on her back she hiked down from Jerusalem to stand on Shepherd's Field and sing. The emotion of that moment was present on her face.

A baby slept, strapped in the backpack of his father. This place and time were of no account to that child, except as in years to come when on Christmas Eve it would be said, "You slept this night in the place where Jesus, himself, once slept."

A girl, aged 11, sat upon the ground and sang the songs, pulling a blue knit cap down to keep the chill air from her neck. It was getting cold, with the sun over the Western hill. Julie, too, was cold. Did she think at that moment of the baby Jesus feeling the same cold night air that blew along the shepherd's field and into the cave?

Another girl, aged 8, wearing a brown furry hat, watched soldiers walk along the low stone wall. These soldiers in the casual dress of the Israeli army were quite unlike the soldiers

42

of Herod's army that also marked these fields, searching for all the newborn babies of the region. Distant, toughened by their life of threatening war, they did not sing "Silent Night, Holy Night." Instead, they listened for the different sounds in the silent nights, and watched for the unholy terror that could burst upon the crowd. Yet, to Ellen, soldiers on duty were just people, like us, part of the crowd choosing to be there on this Christmas Eve. Would that it were the case — that life really would be as it appears to the eyes of children.

The carols and scriptures were completed in too short a time. Those who had arrived in the field early were near the cave entrance. With the benediction they walked deeper into the cave, exiting by steps cut in modern times. There was a hushed moment as we now walked into the cave, stooping, seeing stone surfaces reflect the light of the single electric bulb. It was quiet, as only a mysterious holy moment can be quiet. "For unto you is born this night a Savior who is Christ the Lord."

We walked up from the cave. Some hummed the carols of Christmas, one with eyes moist, handkerchief in hand. Some walked hand in hand, pausing now and then as if to slow their retreat. There were the old and young, the poor and rich, perhaps the hungry, certainly the well fed, the sound and crippled. They all entered the cave singly, bringing to that place and moment their own gifts of expectation. And from the cave, they climbed then to the rocky path leading out of the dark field. Back to the village of Beit Sahur. It was very dark now. Christmas Eve of 1974. The ride back to Jerusalem was swift and quiet. We did not talk much. Instead, we sorted out the steps just taken.

Others walk those steps every Christmas Eve. They are new pilgrims to those special spots made sacred by traditions and dreams. Yet, you do not need to be there to experience the holiness of the Silent Night. Wherever you are, you can be hushed to silence in the presence of that spirit-Child. You can leave the ordinary and make the journey to the Gift of God.

You can bow down in homage. You can recognize the importance of the Moment — for the ages and for you. Christ the Savior is born. Christ your Savior is born.

Silent Night, Holy Night,
All is calm, all is bright
Round yon virgin mother and child,
Holy infant so tender and mild,
Sleep in heavenly peace,
Sleep in heavenly peace.

God's Choice

*"She wrapped him in swaddling clothes,
and laid him in a manger . . ."*

(Luke 2:7)

Eternal God, Creator of Life and Creator of the Christ Child, once more the anniversary of His birth comes close to us. We sing the songs and send the cards and sense the Season. But what is Your message in the festivity?

In meditative moments we are glad for Your revelation in the little child of the manger. We are not used to valuing the vulnerable, the small, the weak. We have been carefully taught that might makes right; the bigger, the better; in strength is our security. Yet, Creator God, You chose a baby. You entered our lives through the pains of motherhood and the dependence of a little newborn infant. Our world has not been the same since. For Your gift we are deeply thankful people.

We confess, though, that we do not pay attention. We confess to ignorance of You and the powers for life that You have given. Our world goes about its clamor for power and might while You call us to care. Our world pushes forward trillions of dollars to kill as You call us to forgive and serve. Our egos strain for the latest gagets and games as You call us to stop building the bigger barns for our needless accumulations.

It was Your baby, Eternal God, who came to redeem, to make right, to release us from all the things that we have turned into our prisons. Yet Your baby Jesus will not force us to do anything. We call him sweet and gentle and so very beautiful but hesitate to go on and call him honest and right and forceful and true and all those other realities that make him our Lord and Savior.

Yet we sing the songs again, and hear the scripture story of the vulnerable and the gentle. Our prayer is for renewed understanding and commitment — and a giving of what we are to what, with that Christ Child, we can be. Help us with such gift-giving, O Eternal and Loving Creator. Amen